Written and illustrated by
Zack Giallongo

DEAN

First published in Great Britain 2018
by Dean, an imprint of Egmont UK Limited,
The Yellow Building, 1 Nicholas Road, London W11 4AN

© & TM 2018 LUCASFILM LTD. All rights reserved.

ISBN 978 0 6035 7490 0
68656/002
Printed in Great Britain

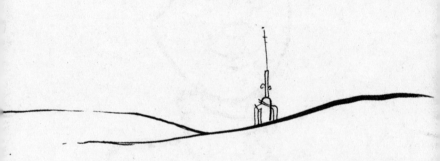

Use circles to draw Tatooine's twin suns
— or however many suns you want!

Draw Leia's new hairstyle!

What strange gadget did Chewie find on the

Millennium Falcon?

What does the inside of the Sarlacc pit look like?

Is it scary?

Or cosy?

Draw Yoda's new hairstyle!

Use zigzags to draw Lando's moustache.

Oh, no! Draw an asteroid field!

Dress up the droids!

Jabba wants you to draw a tattoo for him.

Use rectangles and circles to
add to the Lars homestead.

Give Han Solo

a disguise.

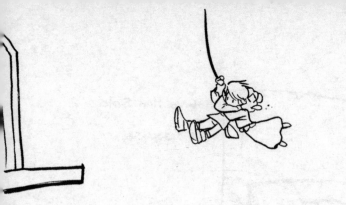

What are Luke and Leia swinging over?

R2-D2 just got a bunch of new attachments.

Draw them!

Decorate this stormtrooper's helmet
any way you like!

Draw the stormtroopers' blaster fire!

PEW!

PEW!

PEW!

PEW!

Draw Obi-Wan Kenobi's beard.

What does a dianoga look like beneath all the
water, sludge and trash?

Darth Vader's TIE fighter needs wings!

Draw the coolest wings ever.

Grand Moff Tarkin is sporting a very fancy
moustache these days, don't you think?

Draw Coruscant's bustling skyline.

Chewie didn't receive his medal
at the Battle of Yavin.
Draw one to cheer him up!

What do you think of C-3PO's new body?

What did Yoda lift out of
the swamp with the Force?

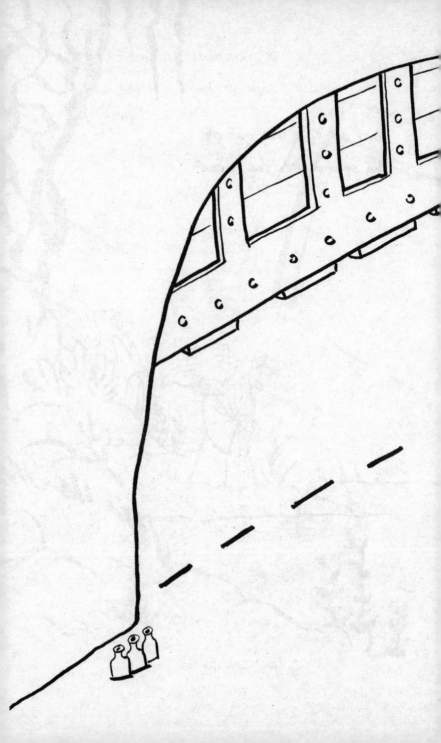

Draw whoever is answering the
door at Jabba's palace ...

and draw a welcome mat.

Make holochess characters
that will help Chewie win.

Max Rebo just got
new instruments
for the band!

Use circles and squares to draw
Darth Vader's new chest plate.

An air guitar is not enough for Mon Mothma.

Draw her a real one so she can join Max Rebo's band!

Something huge is trying to eat
the *Millennium Falcon*!

Draw lines to show how fast the
speeder bikes are going!

Give this stormtrooper some way-cool armour modifications.

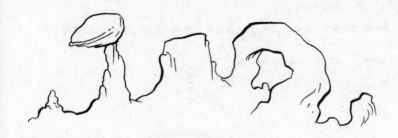

Put some cool sunglasses on everyone, and don't forget to trick out the landspeeder!

Now that Luke Skywalker is a Jedi, he wants some cool sideburns.

What are these bounty hunters snacking on during their break?

>GONK< Draw squares to finish this power droid. >GONK<

Who is under this hood?

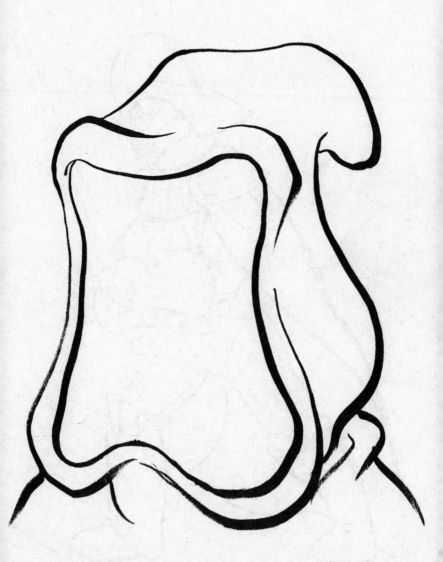

Drat! Luke misplaced his lightsaber.
Draw him something else to use to
battle the Dark Lord of the Sith!

Fill Cloud City with clouds and starships.

Add fur to Han's hood and his tauntaun.

Luke and Biggs find many womp
rats in Beggar's Canyon.

Draw more of these
vicious creatures.

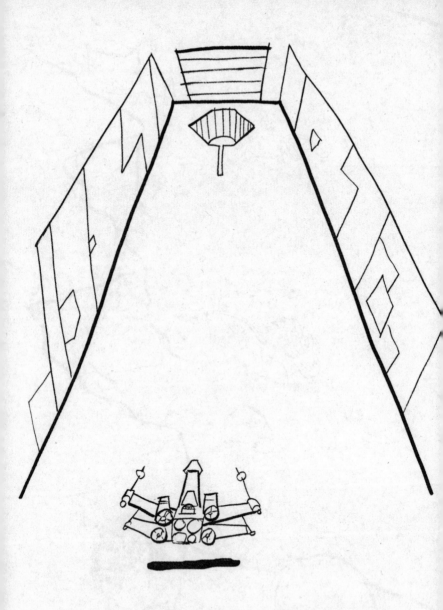

Draw the torpedo hurtling
towards the ventilation shaft!

Draw lines to make a bridge for Obi-Wan to walk across to disable the Death Star's tractor beam.

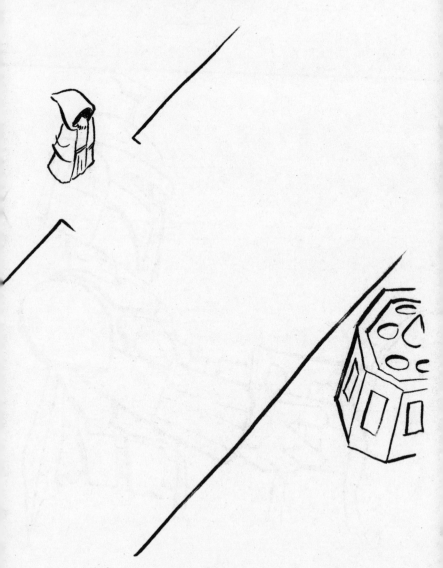

Happy birthday, Boba! What is his present?

Who is Garindan spying on in Mos Eisley?

Put some cool decorations and insignia
on this pilot's helmet.

Colour in Captain Phasma's cape and use stars to show how shiny and polished her armour is.

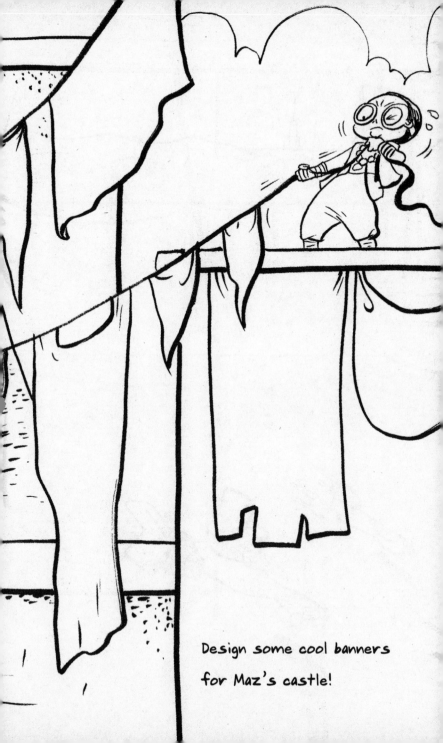

Design some cool banners
for Maz's castle!

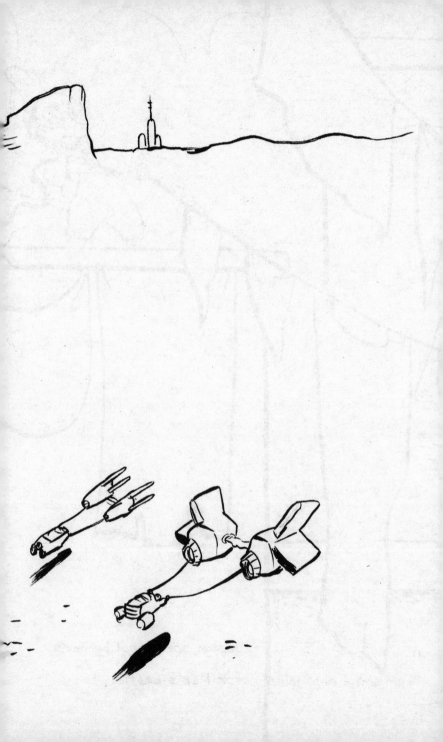

Draw some obstacles for the podracers to avoid.

Help Rey through the maze
to find Master Luke.

Darth Maul is already scary, but can you make him scarier by designing new face markings?

Hux just needs a friend. Draw one for him!

Count Dooku is trying out some new beard styles. Help him out!

Finn is so thirsty in the Jakku desert.

Draw him a tasty beverage.

Draw an ace rebel pilot in this X-wing.

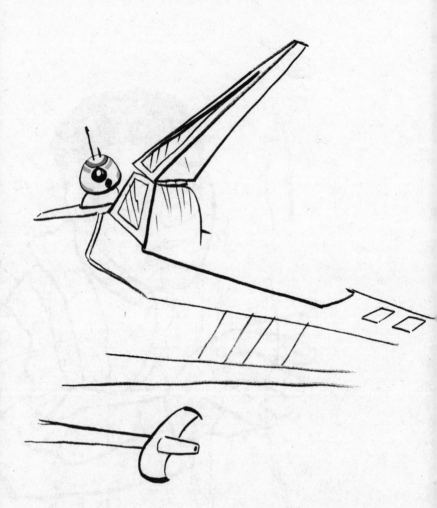

Give this Wookiee warrior a cool fur pattern.

Time to give your old pal Ziro the Hutt
a new design on his body.

Kylo Ren is deep in thought on Starkiller Base,
but what is he thinking about?

Decorate this clone trooper's helmet.

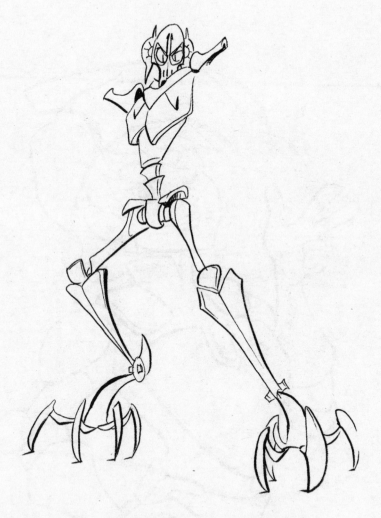

General Grievous has four missing arms.

Draw them in!

Sabine has some rad new colours in
her hair, and cool new armour to match.

That was close! Who are Finn and
Poe hiding from?

Cover this dewback in scaly skin!

What do Luke and Biggs

see up in the sky?

What is hanging up in the wampa's cave?

Draw the slimy space slug that lives in this meteor.

Draw tentacles on the rathtar.

Who else does it have in its grasp?

Give these clone troopers some cool hairstyles.

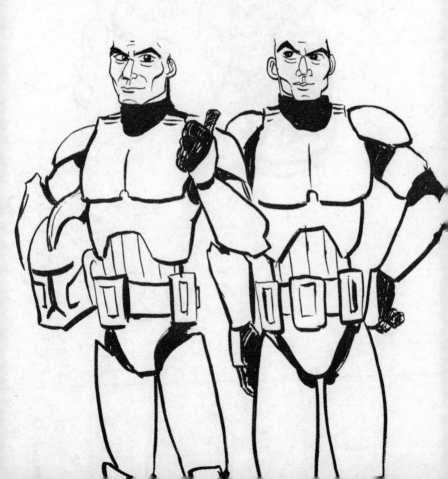

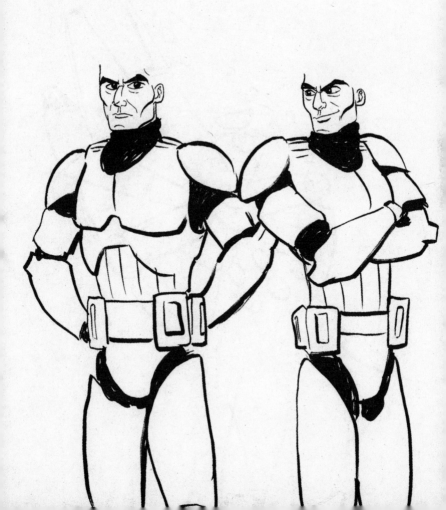

Customise the Millennium Falcon with some cool new features.

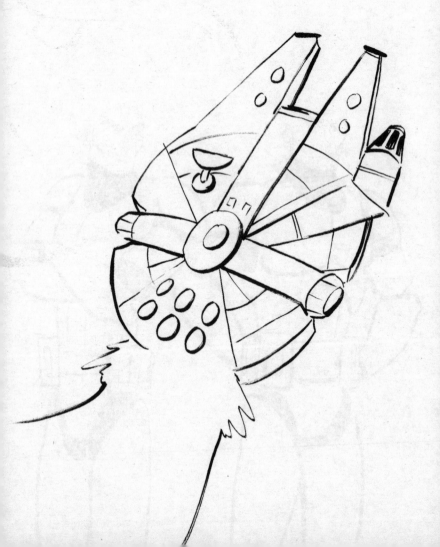

Who is at the end of Jabba's chain?

Draw bridges, ropes and ladders so the Ewoks can get around.

Give this wampa some scary horns!

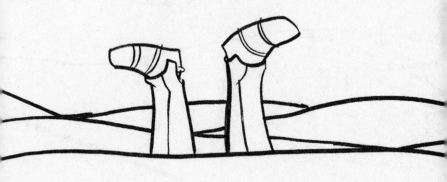

HELP! Draw a hero to pull C-3PO out of the Dune Sea.

Something is stalking Luke on his tauntaun.

What is it?

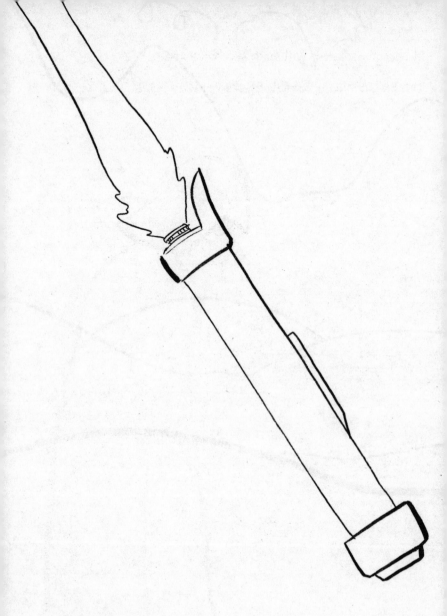

Design this lightsaber handle. Add lots of
different shapes to the hilt to make it look cool!

Lounging about will not be tolerated!

What did Vader catch the stormtroopers doing?

Give Ki-Adi Mundi a humongous hat.

Use boxes to draw Snoke's throne.

Which sinister person is
addressing the First Order?

Hondo Ohnaka is hunting for treasure.

What riches is he about to get his hands on?

Use lines to show Lux the way to Ahsoka.

Draw the Death Star blowing up.
BOOM!